PIANO COURSE FOR BEGINNERS by BARBARA KIRKBY-MASON
FIRST ALBUM Part 2

As well as eleven solo pieces, the First Album Part 2 contains two duets. Daily exercises and a study are included at the beginning and first steps in theory at the end of this book. A keyboard guide, work headings, revision notes and the Reference Pages are additional aids.

Use **First Duet Album** in conjunction with First Album Parts 1 and 2.

Klavierlehrgang für Anfänger von BARBARA KIRKBY-MASON
I. ALBUM Teil 2

Neben 11 Solo-Vortragsstücken enthält das Erste Album, Teil 2, zwei Stücke zum Vierhändigspielen. Tägliche Übungen und eine Etüde befinden sich zu Beginn des Heftes, während die ersten Schritte zur Musiktheorie den Abschluß bilden. Eine Klaviatur-Übersicht, Lern- und Wiederholungsanweisungen neben den Titelüberschriften sowie die Nachschlage-Seiten bieten zusätzliche Stützen.

Parallel zum ERSTEN ALBUM, Teil 1 und 2, empfiehlt sich der Gebrauch des Ersten Albums vierhändig.

Cours de piano pour débutants par BARBARA KIRKBY-MASON
PREMIER ALBUM Partie 2

De même que les onze pièces pour solo, le Premier Album Partie 2 contient deux morceaux à quatre mains. Des exercices journaliers et une étude sont inclus au début et les premiers éléments de théorie à la fin de ce livre. Un guide du clavier, des intitulés d'oeuvres, des notes de révision et les pages de référence sont des aides supplémentaires.

Utilisez "Premier Album à quatre mains" conjointement avec Premier Album, parties 1 et 2.

GW00645487

Bosworth

THE STAVE

Write in the Letter Names of all these notes.

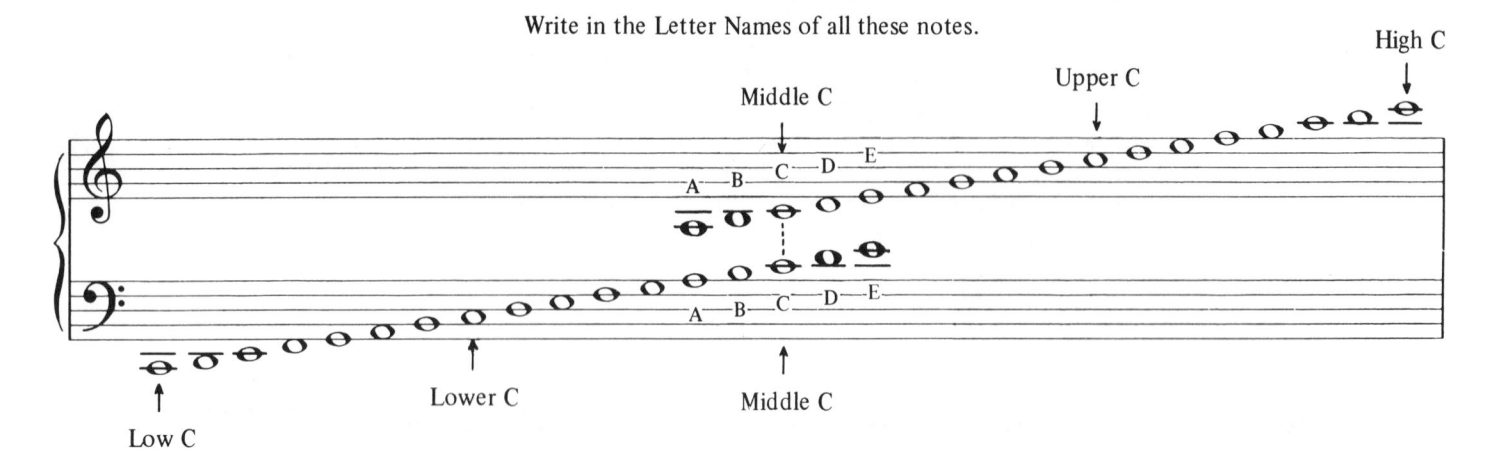

High C

Upper C

Middle C

Middle C

Lower C

Low C

Here is a picture of the Middle Section of your Keyboard.

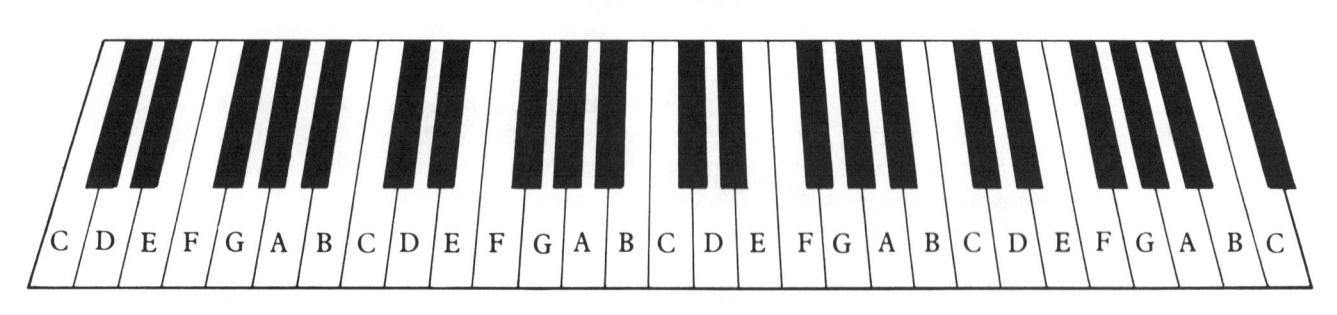

C D E F G A B C D E F G A B C D E F G A B C D E F G A B C

Das Liniensystem

Trage die Namen aller dieser Noten ein.

La Portée

Écrivez en Lettre les Noms de toutes ces notes.

Das eingestrichene (mittlere) C

Do moyen

Das dreigestrichene C

Do supérieur

Das zweigestrichene C

Do aigu

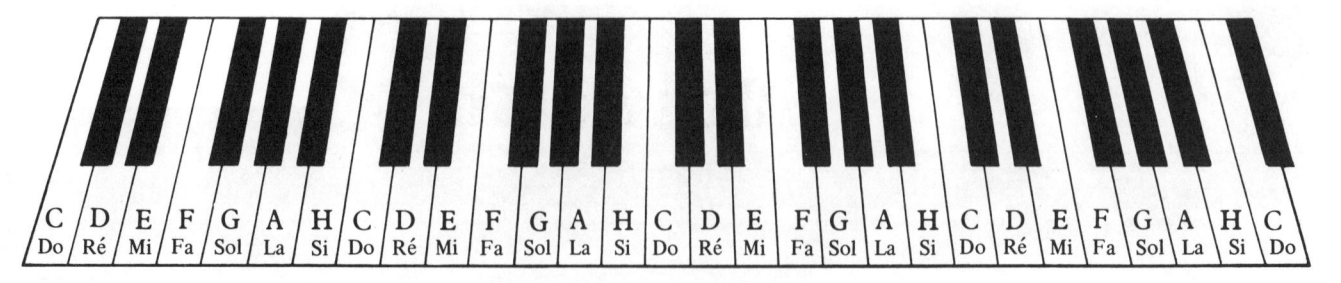

Das große C

Do de la basse

Das kleine C

Do grave

Das eingestrichene (mittlere) C

Do moyen

Hier ist eine Abbildung des mittleren Teils deiner Klaviatur.

Voici une représentation de la partie centrale de votre Clavier.

C D E F G A H C D E F G A H C D E F G A H C D E F G A H C
Do Ré Mi Fa Sol La Si Do Ré Mi Fa Sol La Si Do Ré Mi Fa Sol La Si Do Ré Mi Fa Sol La Si Do

DAILY EXERCISES

To be practised three times legato and three times staccato.

Tägliche Übungen

Dreimal legato und dreimal stakkato zu spielen.

Exercices journaliers

Jouer trois fois legato et trois fois staccato.

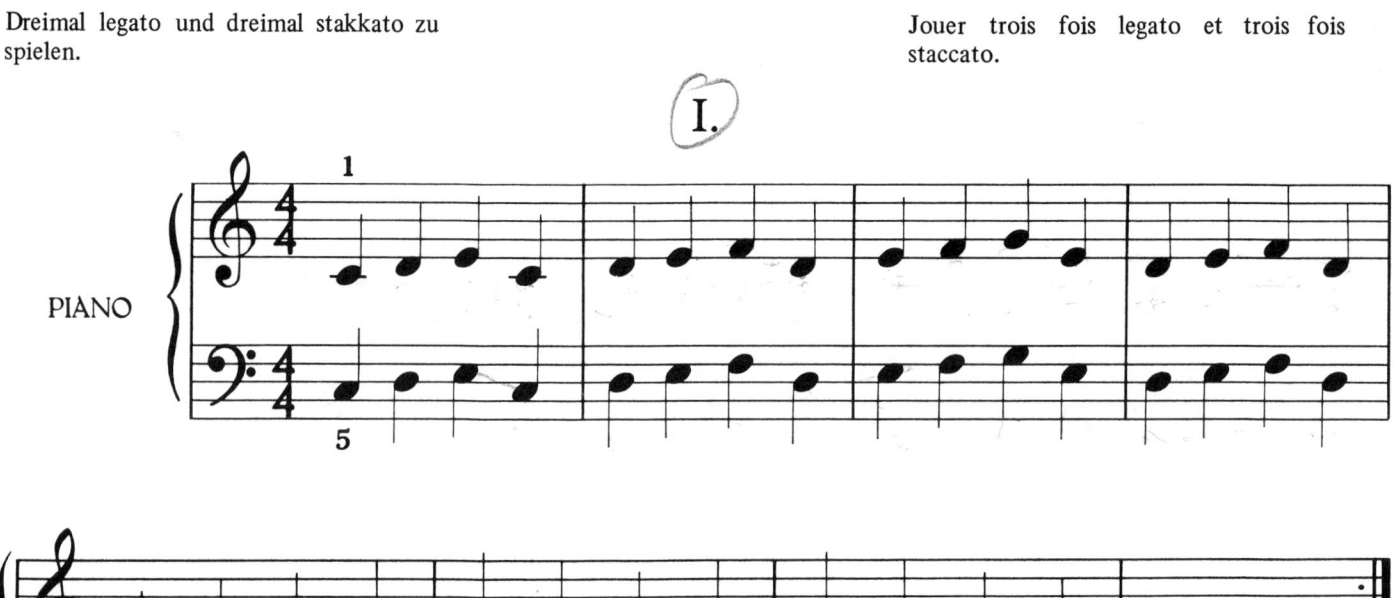

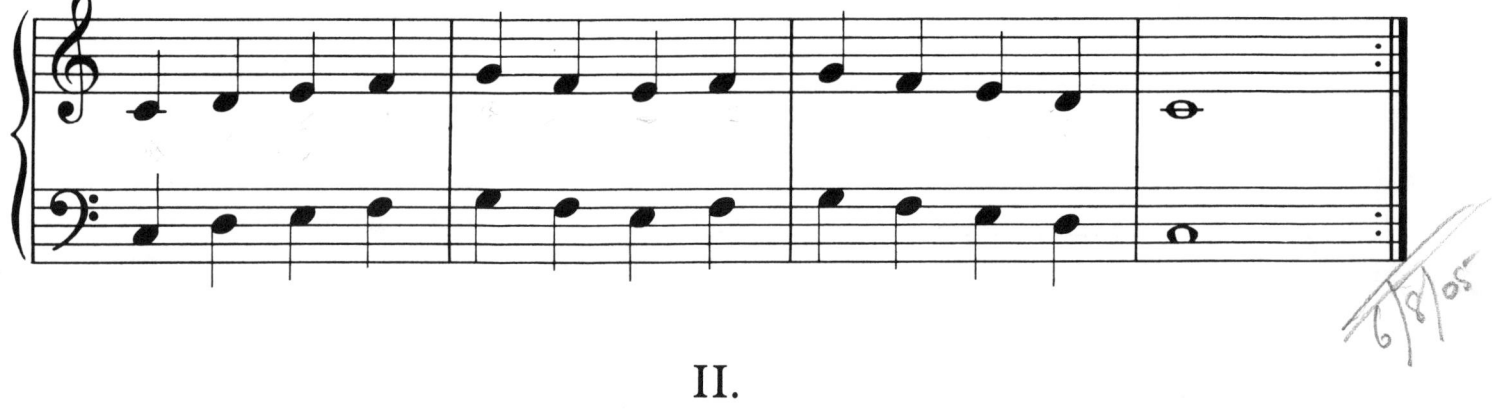

II.

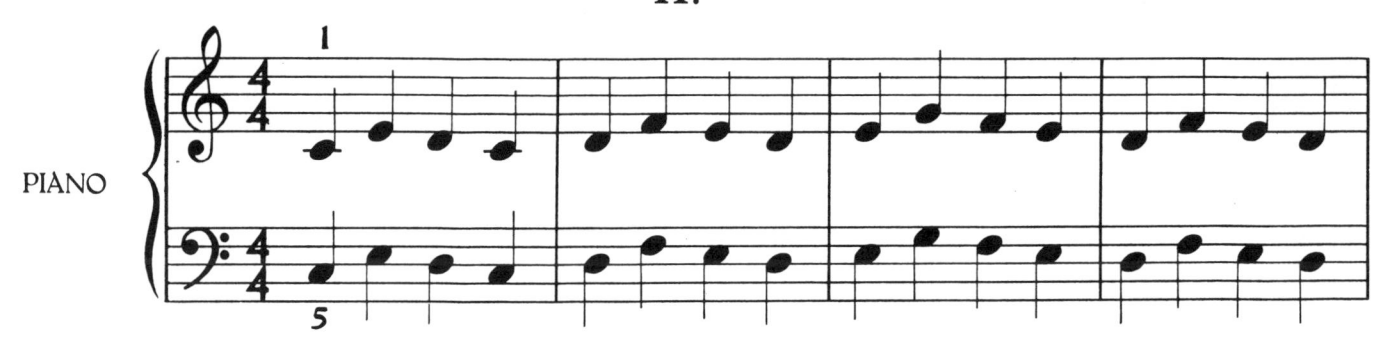

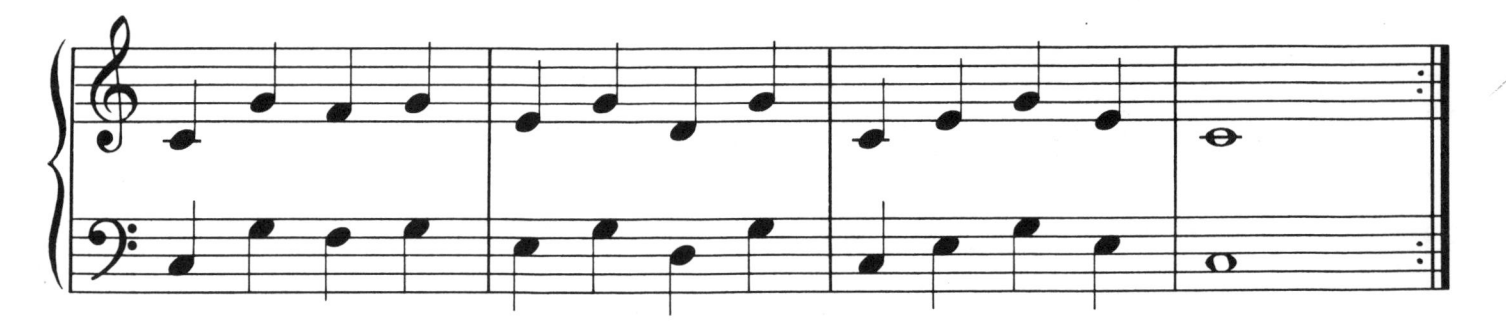

B. & Co. Ltd. 22222

4

ETÜDE in C

ÉTUDE en Do

Spiele gleichmäßig mit festem Finger-spitzenanschlag und gleichbleibender Tongebung.

Play steadily with rounded fingers and even tone.

Jouez constamment avec des doigts fermes et arrondis et une sonorité égale.

Wiederhole: Namen und Zeitwerte von Noten (Teil 1, Seite 3)

Revise: Names and values of notes (Part 1, p. 3)

Revoyez: noms et valeurs des notes (Partie 1, p. 3)

Brightly — Heiter — Gai

B. & Co. Ltd. 22222

ON THE SEA

Am Meer

Sur la mer

TONART C-DUR	KEY C	TON DE DO
Lerne: Daumen-Drehungen in der rechten Hand (Takt 14/15)	*Learn:* Thumb-turns for R.H. (bars 14/15)	*Apprenez:* à faire tourner le pouce pour la main droite (mesures 14/15)
Wiederhole: Gebundene Noten:	*Revise:* Tied notes:	*Revoyez:* notes liées:

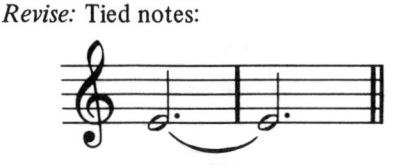

With a swing — Mit Schwung — Avec élan

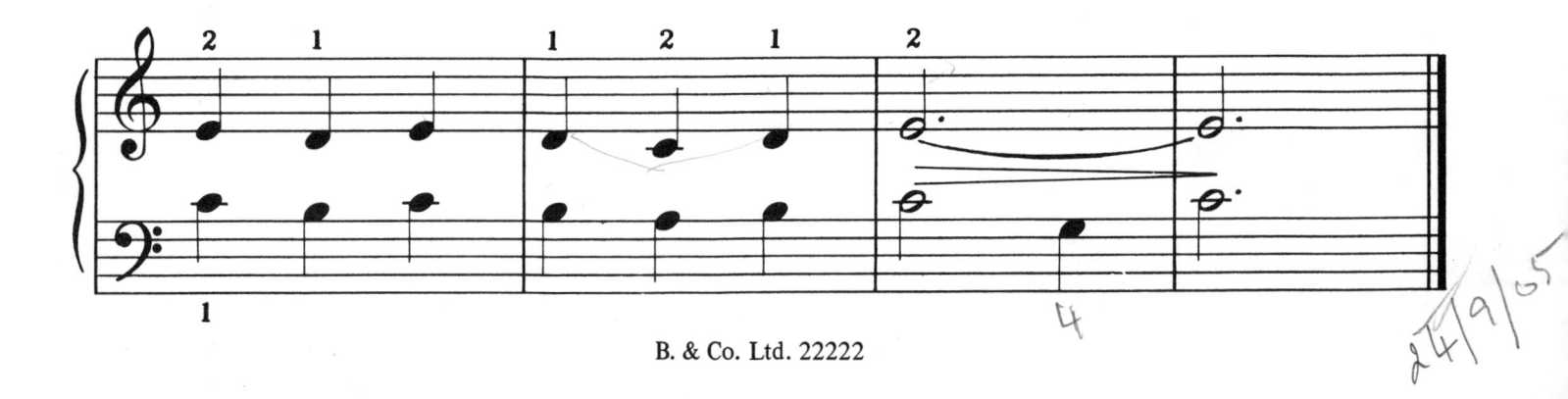

B. & Co. Ltd. 22222

FOLLOW ME!

Komm' mir nach

Suivez-moi

TONART C-DUR	KEY C	TON DE DO

Lerne: Das FIS führt zum G-Akkord (Takte 7 und 8)

Learn: F♯ leads to G chord (bars 7 & 8)

Apprenez: Fa dièse mène à l'accord en sol (mesures 7 & 8)

Wiederhole:

Revise:

Revoyez:

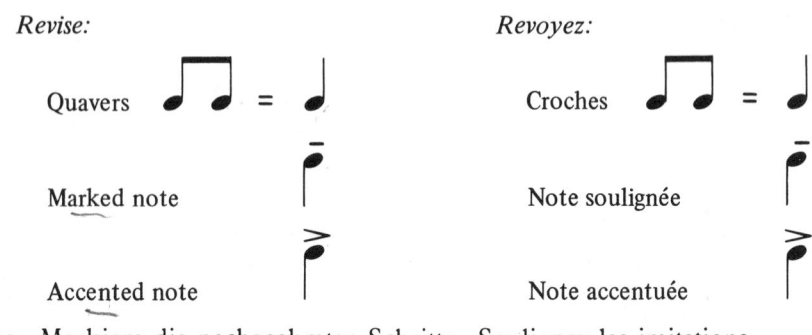

Achtelnoten	Quavers	Croches
Hervorgehobene Note	Marked note	Note soulignée
Akzentuierte (betonte) Note	Accented note	Note accentuée

Mark the imitations—Markiere die nachgeahmten Schritte—Soulignez les imitations

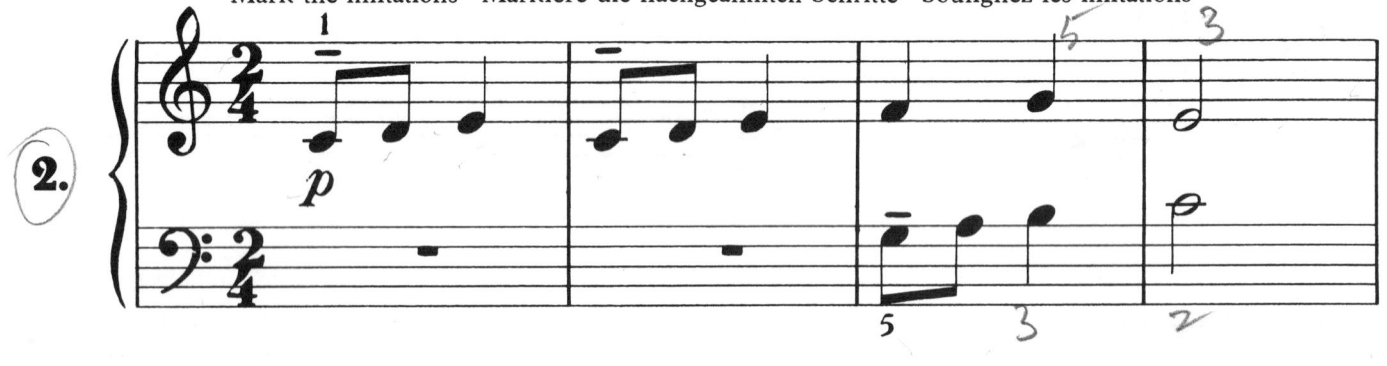

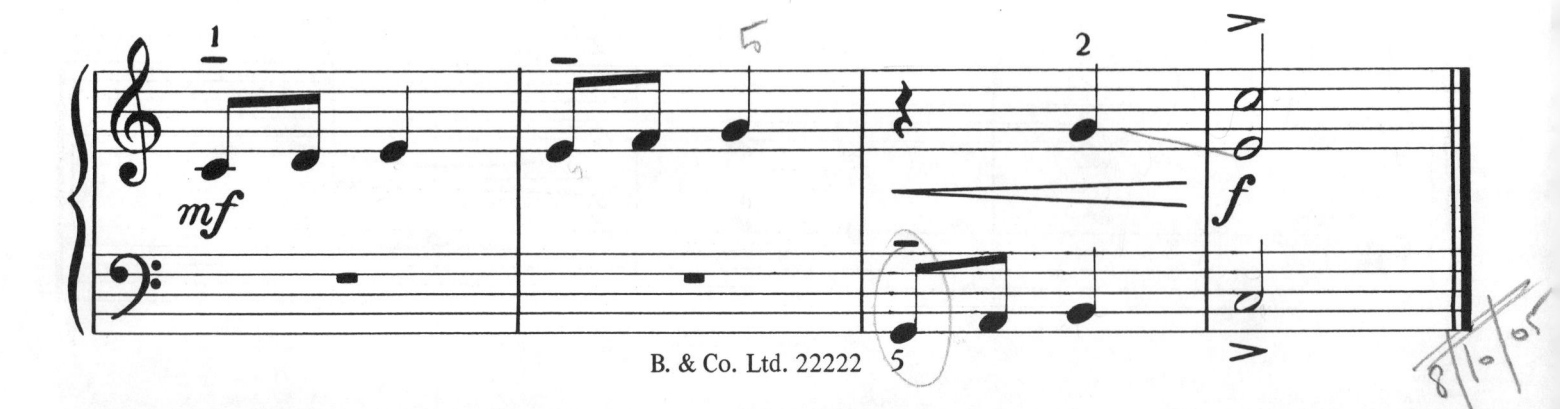

SOLDIERS

Soldaten

Lerne: Die linke Hand fängt mit dem "kleinen C" an.

Neue Akkorde in der linken Hand (Takte 7 u. 8); den C-dur Akkord in der linken Hand des letzten Taktes.

Soldats

Learn: L.H. begins on lower C.
New chords for L.H. (bars 7 & 8).
C triad in L.H. (last bar)

Apprenez: La main gauche commence sur le do grave.
Nouveaux accords pour la main gauche (Mesures 7 & 8); accord sans l'octave en do à la main gauche (dernière mesure)

ff = sehr laut

ff = very loud

ff = très fort

Wiederhole: Takt-Angaben:

Revise: Time signatures:

Revoyez: Mesures:

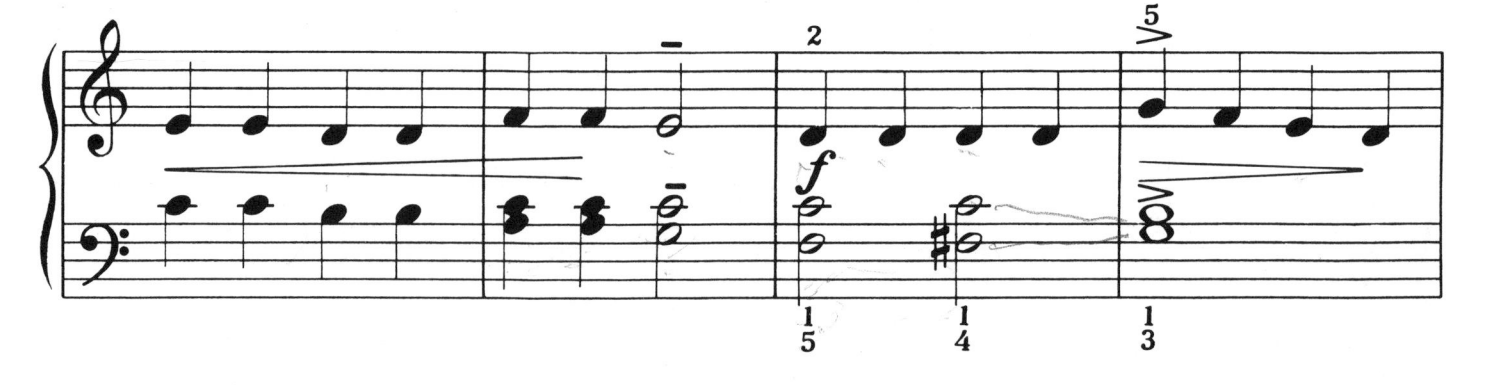

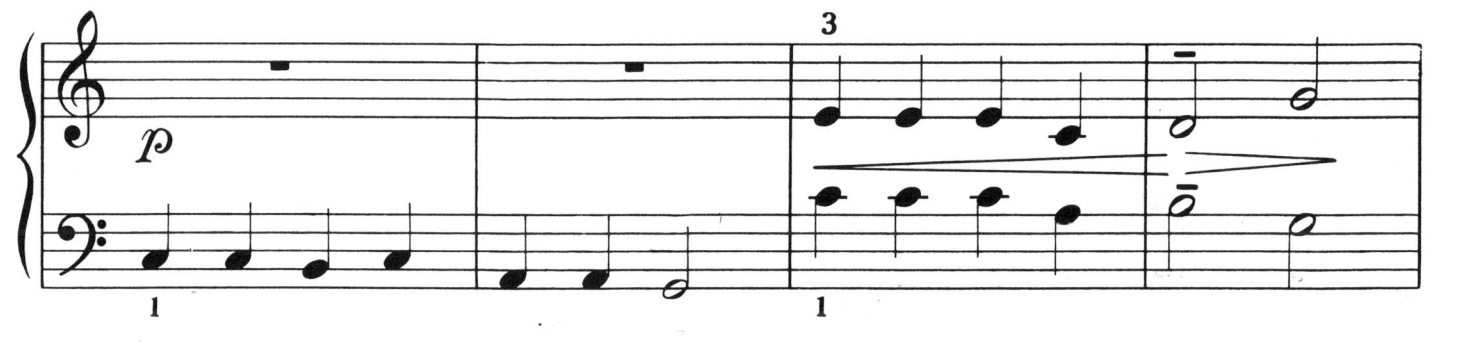

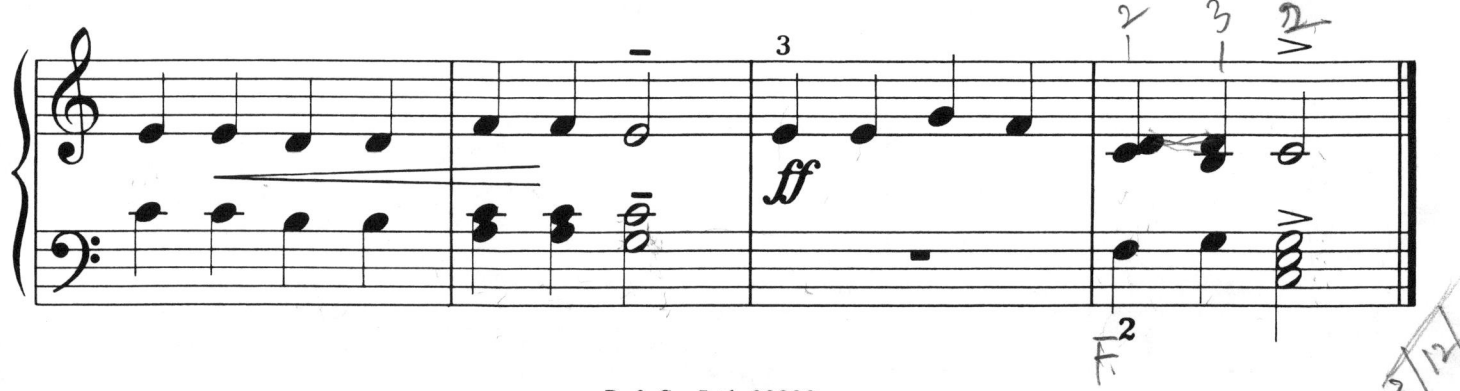

B. & Co. Ltd. 22222

MARCH OF THE DWARFS

Marsch der Zwerge

Marche des nains

Lerne: Eine neue B-Note im 10. Takt: *AS*

Learn: New flat (A♭) (bar 10)

Apprenez: Nouveau bémol (La♭) (mesure 10)

pp = sehr leise

pp = very soft

pp = très doux

Wiederhole:

Revise:

Revoyez:

Staccato-Note

Staccato note

note staccato

spitz abgesetzter Bogen

Lifted slur

lié levé

Versetzungszeichen vor FIS u. B
Auflösungszeichen vor F

Signs F♯ F♮ B♭

signe Fa♯ Fa♮ Si♭

Sechzehntelnoten

Semiquavers

Doubles croches

At a steady pace – Gleichmäßiges Tempo – Avec fermeté

LULLABY in F
Wiegenlied in F
Berceuse en Fa

Lerne: Die rechte Hand fängt mit A an.
Die linke Hand fängt mit F an.

Learn: R.H. begins on A.
L.H. begins on F.

Apprenez: La main droite commence sur La.
La main gauche commence sur Fa.

Wiederhole: Die Tonart F-dur hat ein B-Vorzeichen (B). Finde das B-Auflösungszeichen.

Revise: The F key signature has one flat (B♭). Find B♮ sign.

Revoyez: Le ton de Fa à un bémol (Si♭). Trouvez le ton de Si♮.

Softly and sweetly — Leise und zart — Doux et tendre

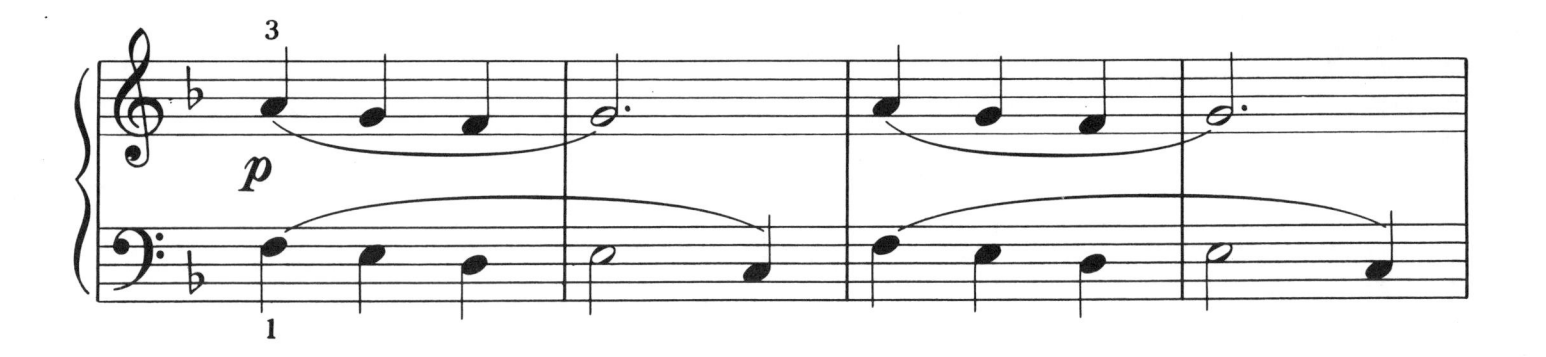

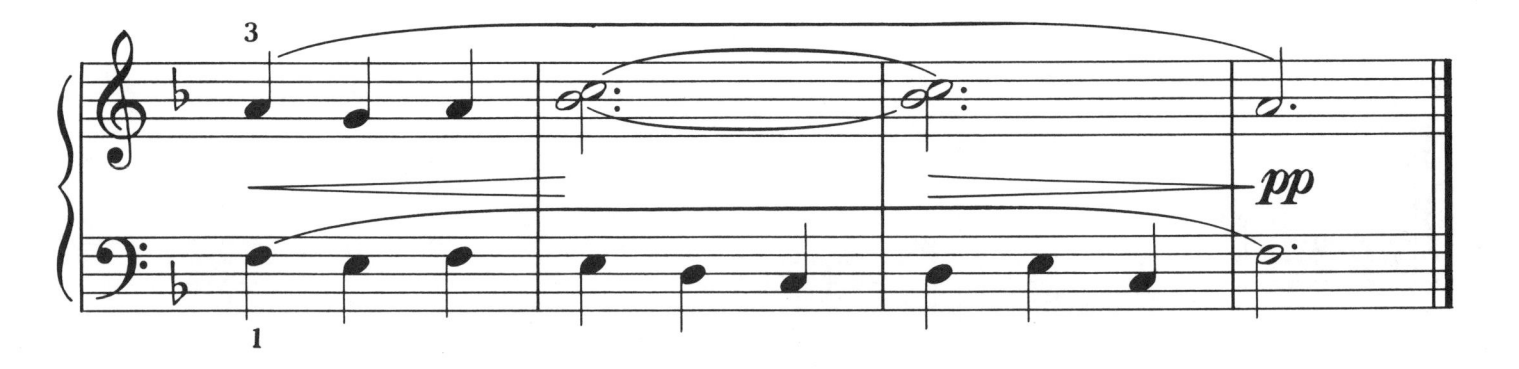

B. & Co. Ltd. 22222

WHITE RABBIT

Weißes Kaninchen

Le petit lapin blanc

TONART G-DUR

Lerne: Die rechte Hand fängt mit G an. Beschließe dieses Stück mit dem G-dur-Akkord.

Wiederhole: Die Tonart G-dur hat ein Kreuz-Vorzeichen (FIS).
Finde CIS sowie die Noten C und F mit vorangestellten Auflösungszeichen in diesem Stück.

KEY G

Learn: R.H. begins on G. End this piece with a G chord.

Revise: The G key signature has one sharp (F♯).
Find C♯ C♮ F♮ in this piece.

TON DE SOL

Apprenez: La main droite commence sur Sol. Terminez cette pièce avec un accord en sol.

Revoyez: Le ton de sol a un dièse (Fa♯).
Trouvez Do♯ Do♮ Fa♮ dans ce morceau.

Fluently — Flüssig — Lié

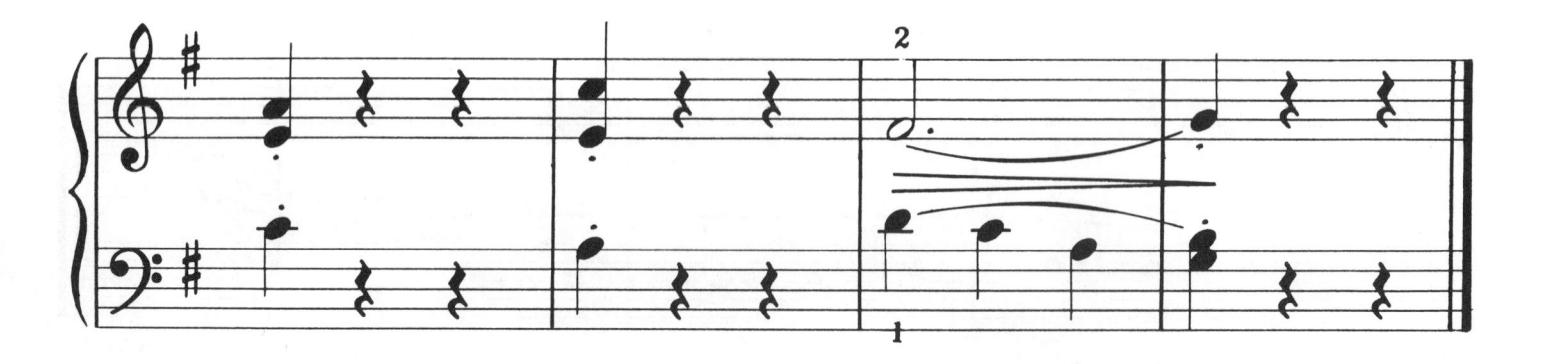

B. & Co. Ltd. 22222

SPRITES

Gespenster

TONART A-MOLL

Lerne: Die rechte Hand fängt mit dem Ton A an. Der A-moll-Akkord beschließt dieses Stück.

Wiederhole: Zeitmuster für Achtel- und Sechzehntelnoten:

KEY A MINOR

Learn: R.H. begins on A. A minor chord ends this piece.

Revise: Quaver and semiquaver time patterns:

Fantômes

TON DE LA MINEUR

Apprenez: La main droite commence sur La. Un accord de La mineur termine ce morceau.

Revoyez: Croche et demi-croche exemples de temps:

Playfully — Spielerisch — En jouant

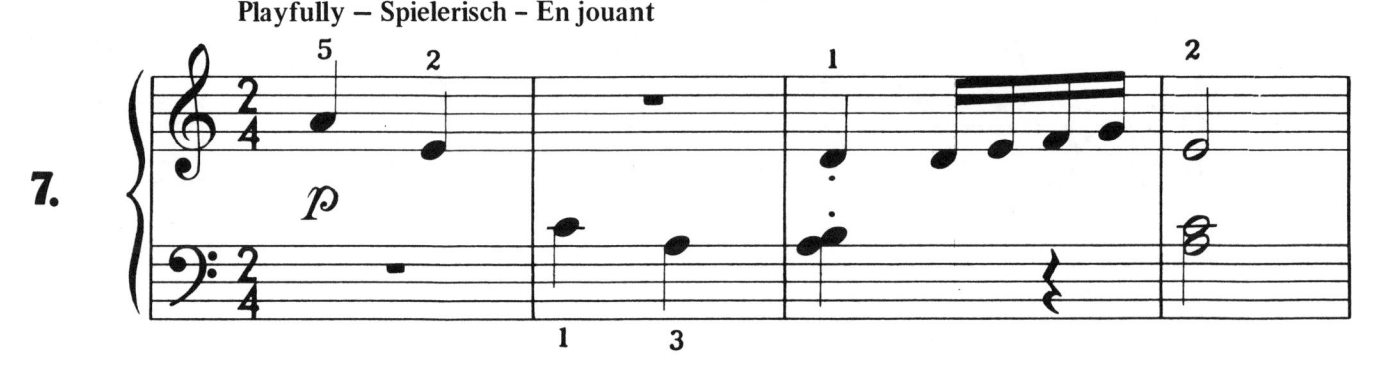

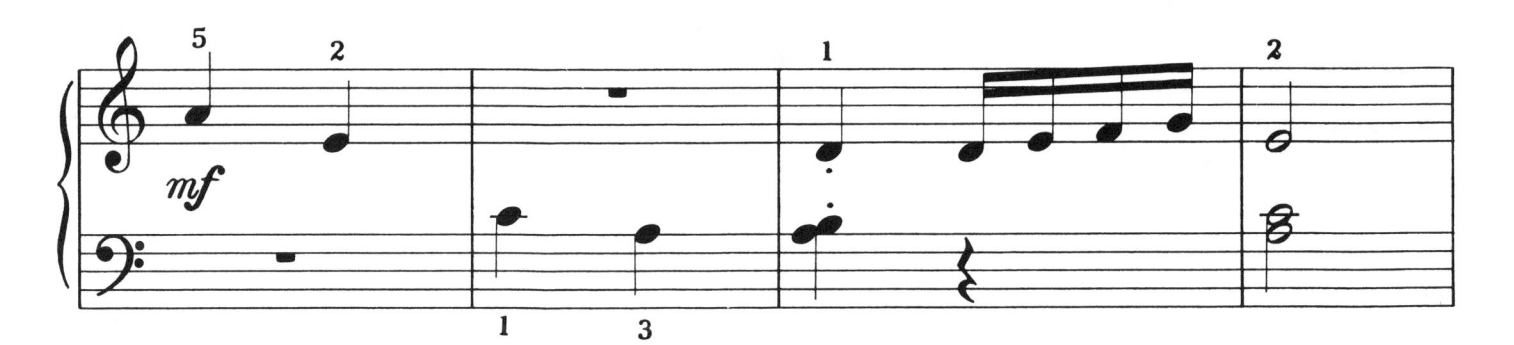

IN THE FOREST

Im Wald

En forêt

TONART D-MOLL

KEY D MINOR

TON DE RÉ MINEUR

Lerne: Der D-moll-Akkord beschließt dieses Stück.

Learn: D minor chord ends this piece.

Apprenez: un accord en ré mineur termine ce morceau.

With expression — Mit Ausdruck — Avec expression

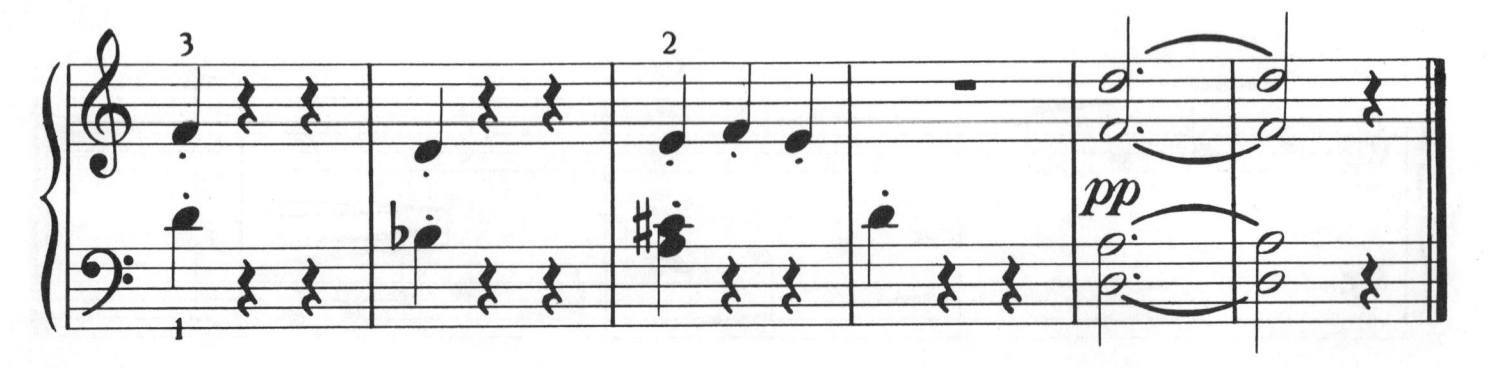

STEAM TRAIN

Die Eisenbahn

Train à vapeur

TONART G-DUR

Klatsche zu diesem 4/4-Takt-Muster:

KEY G

Clap this time pattern:

TON DE SOL

Battez cet exemple de temps:

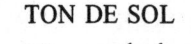
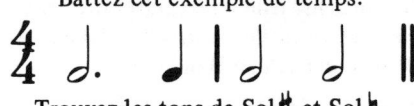

Finde die Versetzungszeichen für GIS und das wieder aufgelöste G.

Find G♯ and G♮ signs.

Trouvez les tons de Sol♯ et Sol♮.

Rhythmically – Rhythmisch – Très rythmé

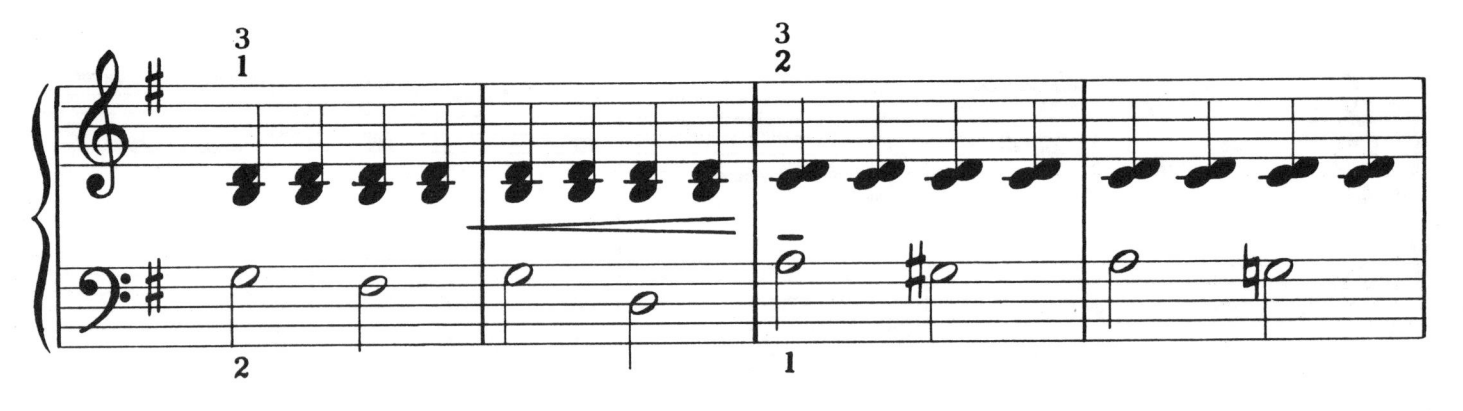

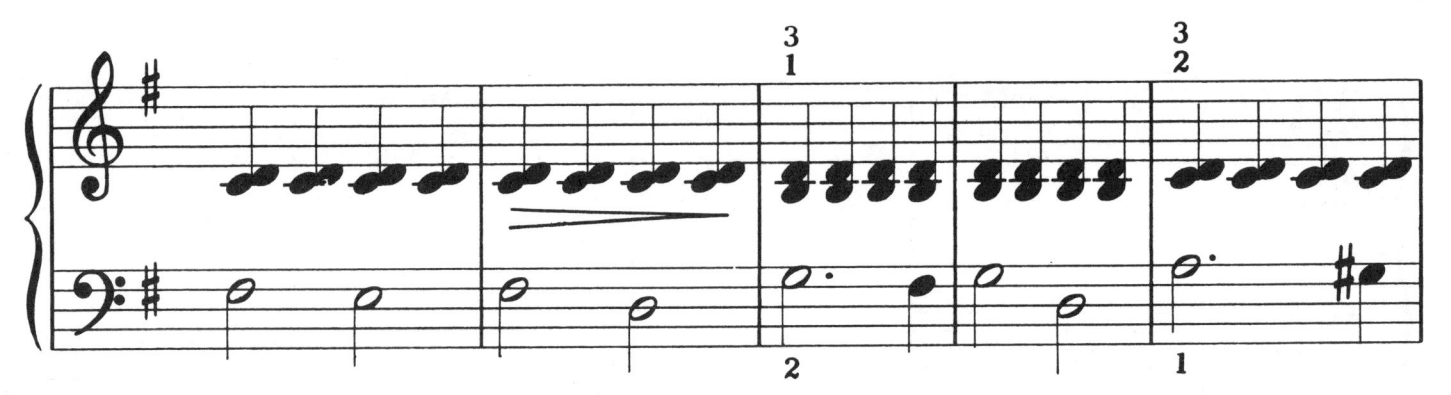

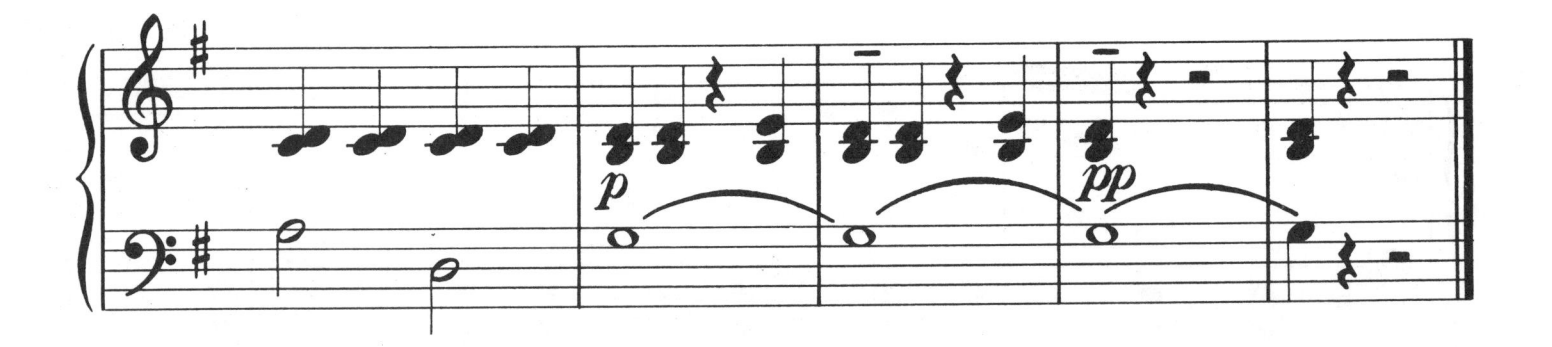

B. & Co. Ltd. 22222

IN THE HIGHLANDS

Im Gebirge

Dans les montagnes

TONART F-DUR

KEY F

TON DE FA

Übe zunächst jede Hand getrennt. Behalte einen gleichmäßigen rhythmischen Anschlag in der linken Hand bei.

Practise hands separately at first. Always keep L.H. beats steady.

Etudiez les mains séparément d'abord. Maintenez toujours constants les battements de la main gauche.

Wiederhole: die Pausenzeichen

Revise: Rests

Revoyez: Silences

With spirit – Geistvoll – Plein d'esprit

10.

CHIMES

Glocken

Carillon

Lerne: Beide Hände spielen im Violinschlüssel. Hebe die Hand vor den Viertelpausen deutlich ab.

Learn: Both hands play in the treble. Lift hand off for crotchet rests.

Apprenez: Les deux mains jouent en clé de sol. Levez les mains pour les silences de noires.

With a bell-like tone — Mit glockenähnlichem Tom — Comme un chant de cloches

SKATERS' WALTZ in C
Duet

Schlittschuhläufer-
Walzer in C
4 händig

Les patineurs
Valse en Do
4 mains

Smoothly — Sanft – Coulant

12. Secondo

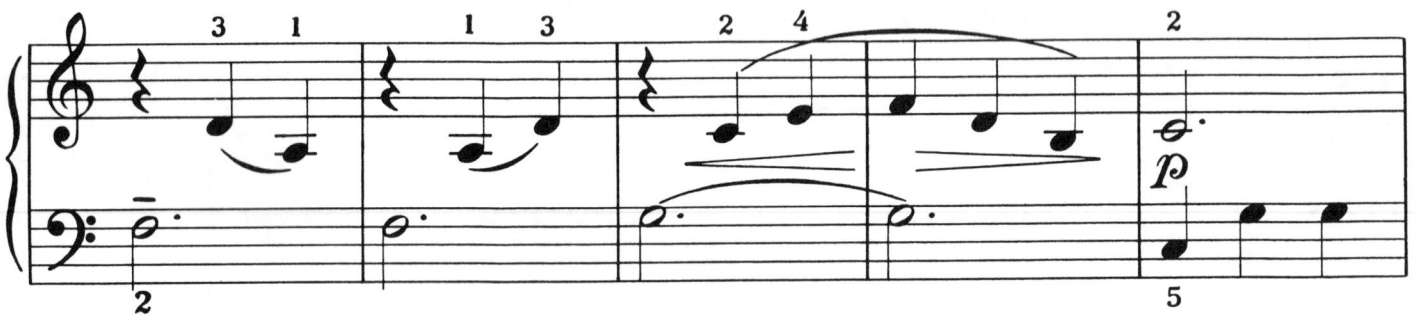

SKATERS' WALTZ in C
Duet

Schlittschuhläufer-
Walzer in C
4 händig

Les patineurs
Valse en Do
4 mains

Smoothly — Sanft — Coulant

12. Primo

HORNPIPE in G
Duet

Matrosentanz in G
4 händig

Danse de matelots en Sol
4 mains

Dein Partner beginnt auf dem zweiten Taktschlag.

Your partner begins on the second beat of the bar.

Votre partenaire commence sur le second temps de la mesure.

Wiederhole: Triole

Revise: Triplet

Revoyez: Triolet

With spirit — Lebhaft — Vivement

13. Secondo

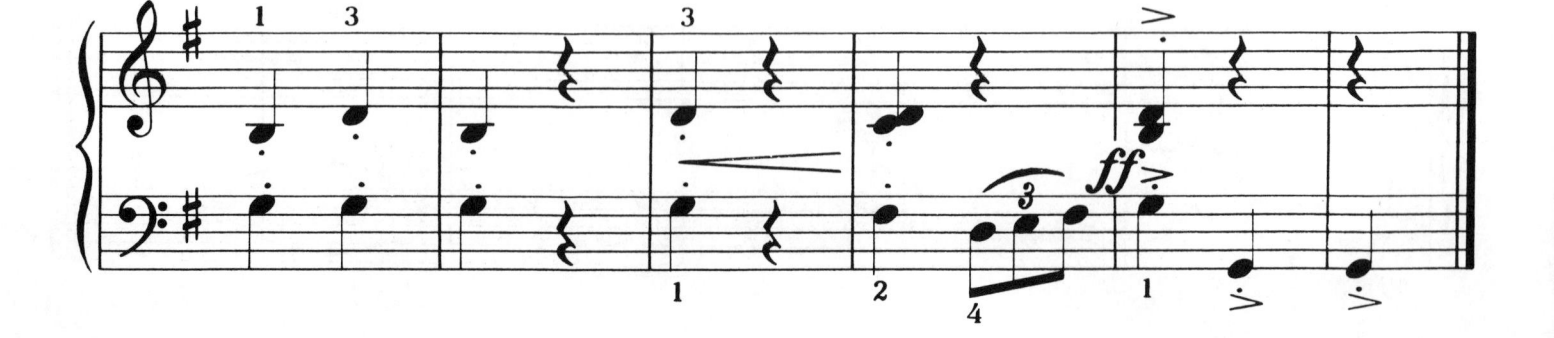

HORNPIPE in G
Duet

Matrosentanz in G
4 händig

Danse de matelots en Sol
4 mains

Die Wiederholung der ersten Notenphrase beginnst du im vierten Takt einen halben Ton höher auf C.

For the repeat of the first pattern you start a note higher on C (bar 4).

Pour répéter le premier exemple vous commencez une note plus haut sur Do (mesure 4).

With spirit − Lebhaft − Vivement

13. Primo

FIRST STEPS IN THEORY

1. Write a line of treble and bass clefs and name them.

Name

2. Copy these notes and rests.

Semibreve   **Minim**   **Dotted Minim**   **Crotchet**

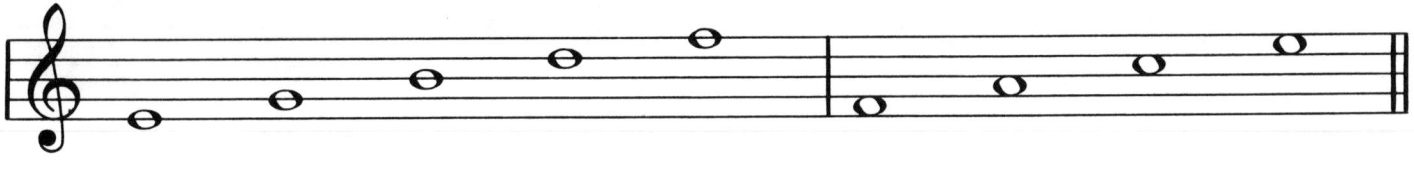

Quaver   **Semiquaver**

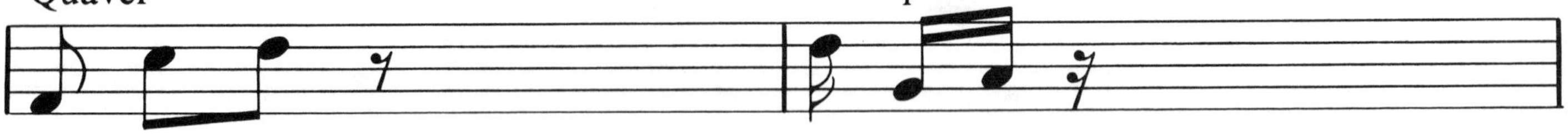

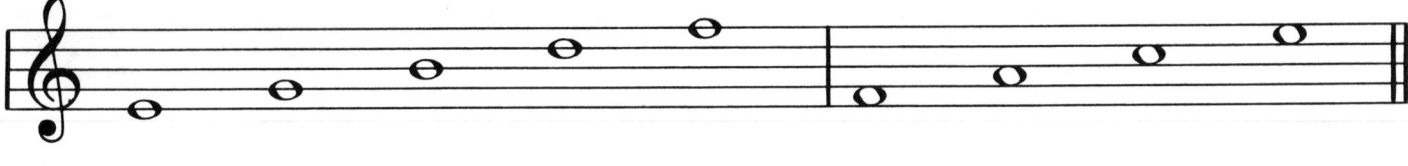

Name

3. Copy lines and spaces in the treble and name them.

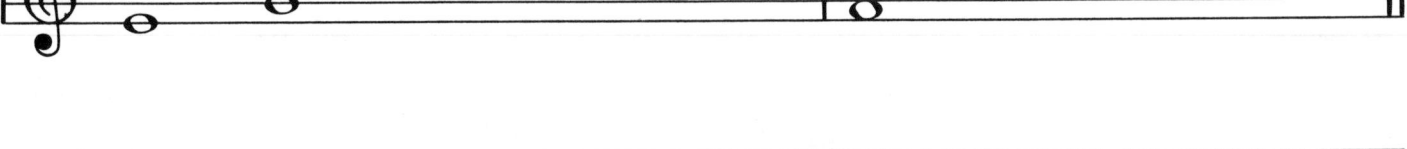

4. Copy lines and spaces in the bass and name them.

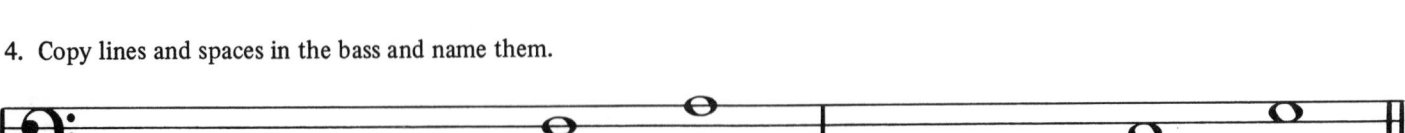

5. Copy the following and name them.

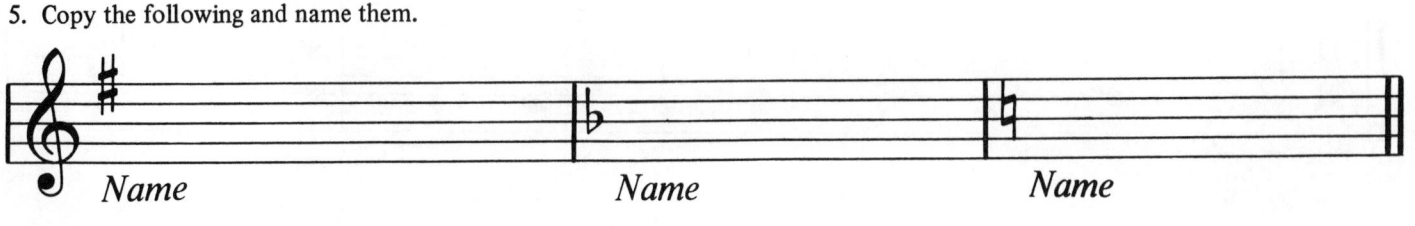

Name   *Name*   *Name*

B. & Co. Ltd. 22222

1. Schreibe je eine Zeile Noten im Violin-und Baß-Schlüssel und nenne sie.

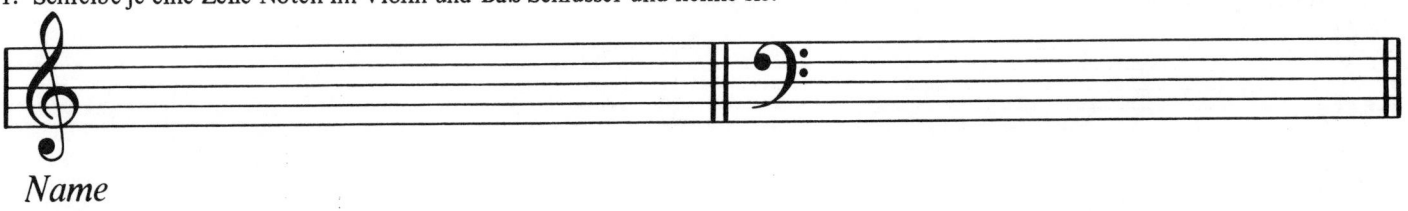

Name

2. Schreibe diese Noten und Pausenzeichen ab.

Ganze   Halbe   Punktierte Halbe (3/4) Viertel

Achtel   Sechzehntel

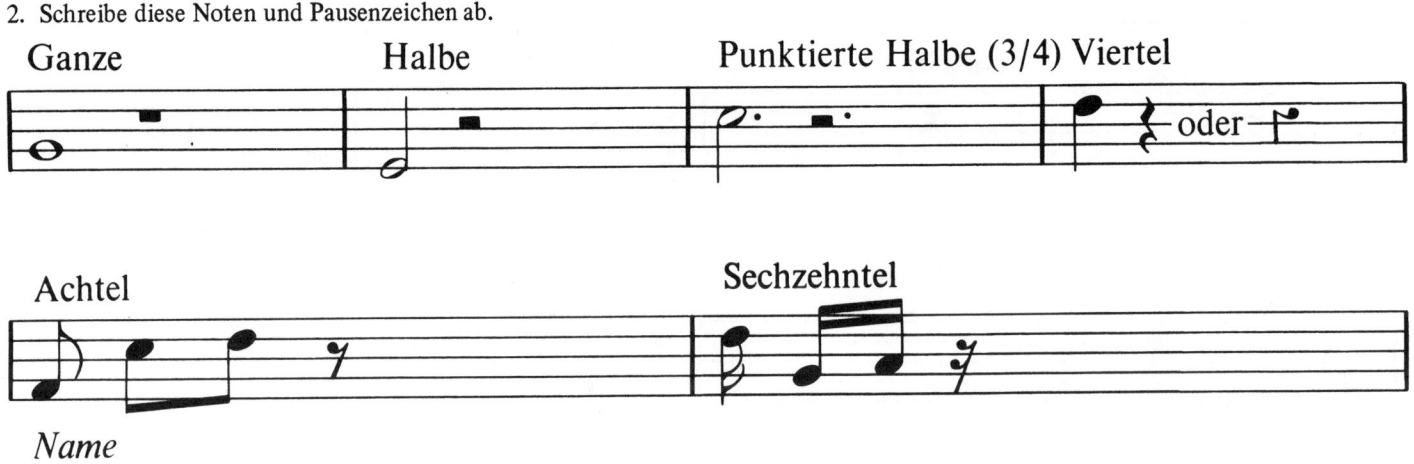

Name

3. Schreibe die Noten auf den Linien und in den Zwischenräumen im Violin-Schlüssel und nenne sie.

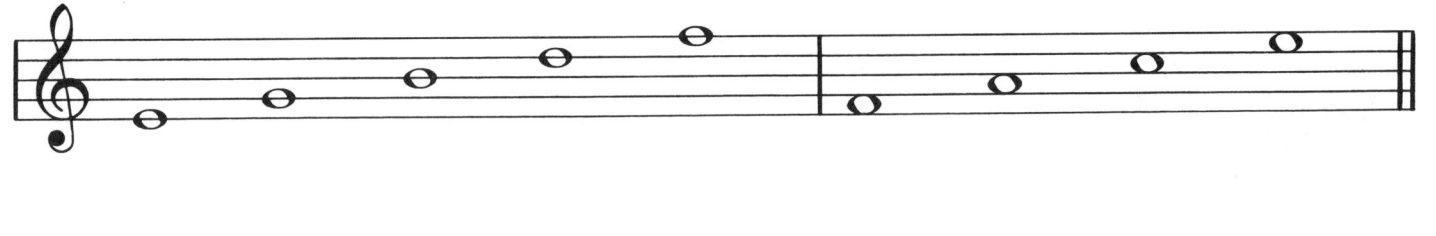

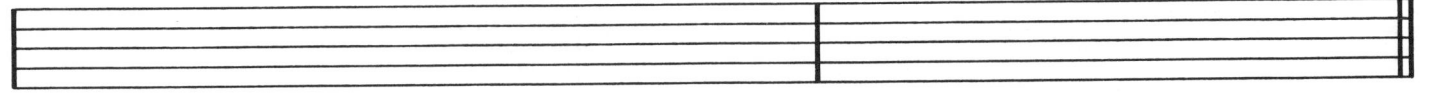

4. Schreibe die Noten auf den Linien und in den Zwischenräumen im Baß-Schlüssel und nenne sie.

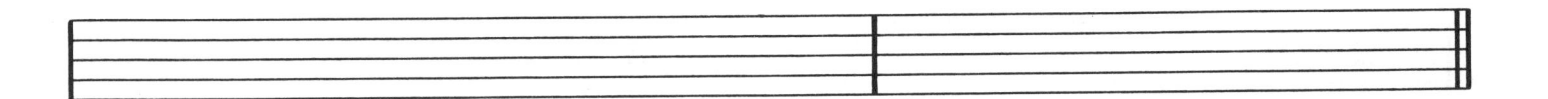

5. Schreibe die folgenden Zeichen und nenne sie.

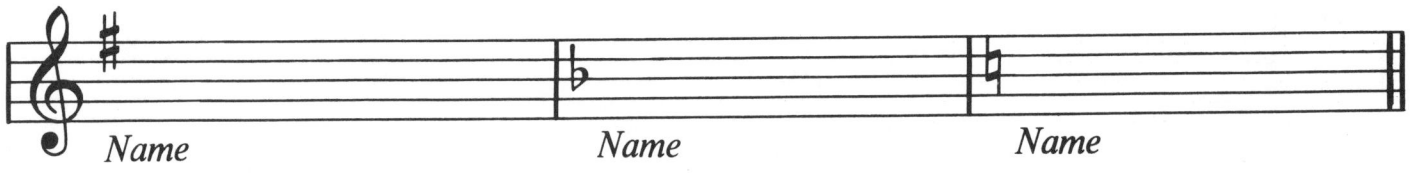

Name   *Name*   *Name*

B. & Co. Ltd. 22222

1. Écrivez une portée de notes en clef de sol et en clef de fa et nommez les.

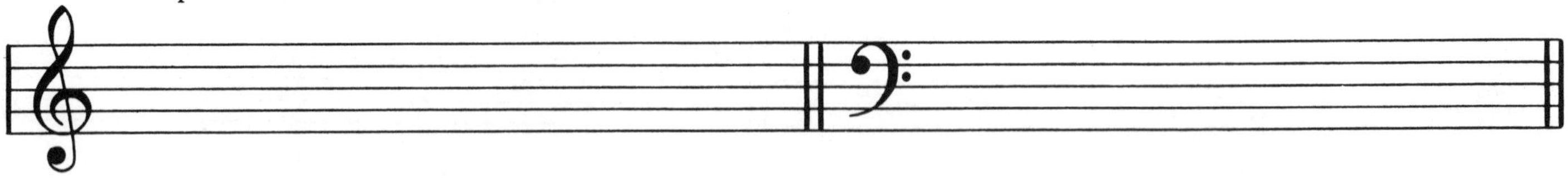

Nom

2. Copiez ces notes et silences.

Ronde   Blanche   Blanche pointée (3/4)   Noire

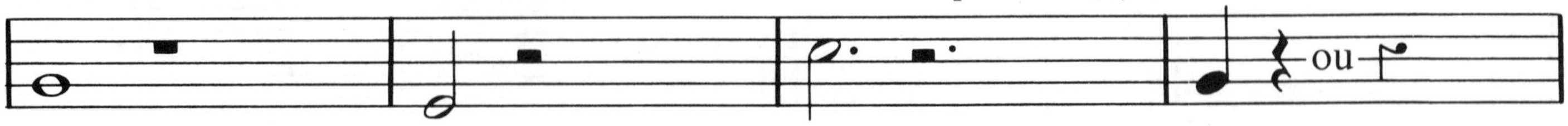

Croche   Double croche

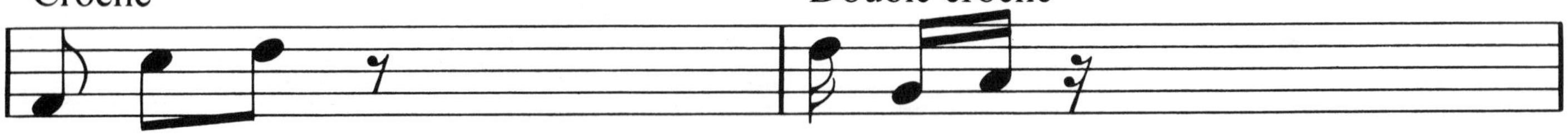

Nom

3. Écrivez et nommez toutes les notes d'une portée en clé de sol.

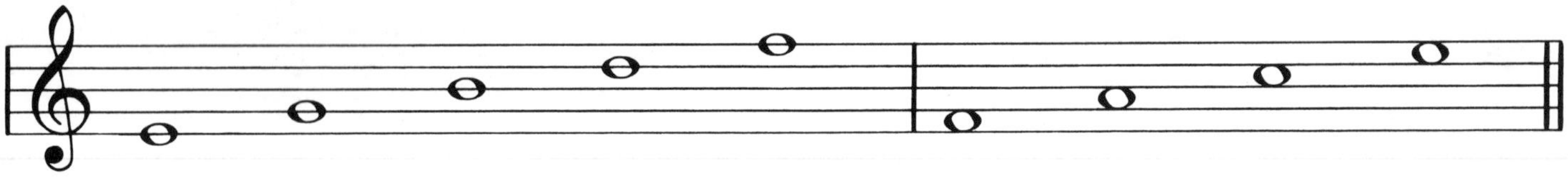

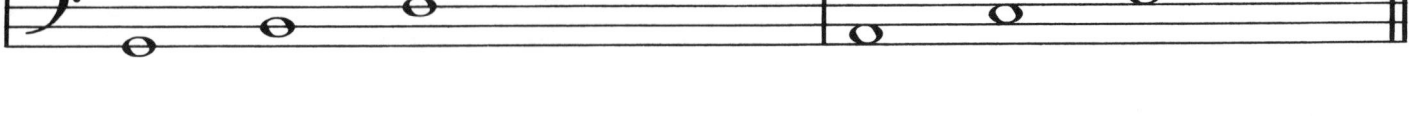

4. Écrivez et nommez toutes les notes d'une portée en clé de fa.

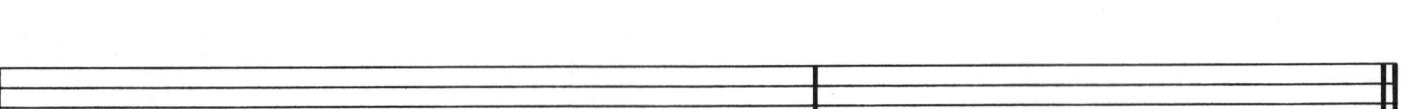

5. Écrivez et nommez les signes suivants.

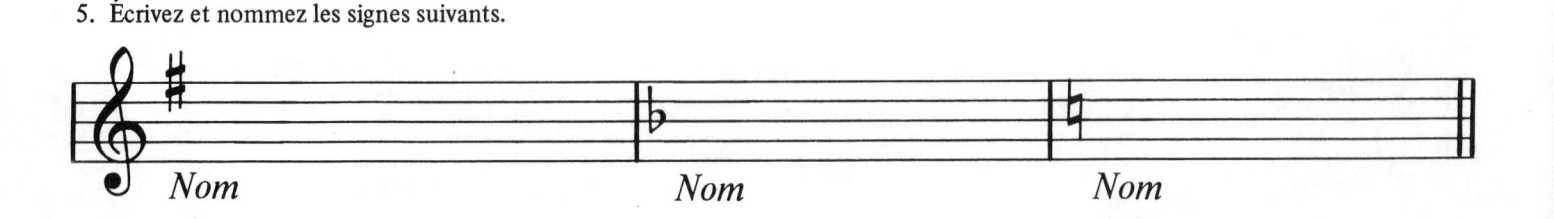

Nom   *Nom*   *Nom*

REFERENCE PAGE
Die Nachschlage-Seite
Page de référence

AUFBAU VON DUR-AKKORDEN	BUILDING MAJOR CHORDS	FORMATION D'ACCORDS EN MAJEUR

(C C Do)　　　　　(F F Fa)　　　　　(G G Sol)

C E G　　　　　F A C　　　　　G B(H) D
Do Mi Sol　　　　Fa La Do　　　　Sol Si Ré

C E G　　　　　F A C　　　　　G B(H) D
Do Mi Sol　　　　Fa La Do　　　　Sol Si Ré

ÜBUNGEN MIT AKKORDEN	CHORD-PRACTICE	EXERCICE D'ACCORD

Etüde (S. 4)　Study (p. 4)　Etude (p. 4)　　　　Am Meer (S. 5)　On the Sea (p. 5)　Sur la mer (p. 5)

1.　　　　　　　　　　**2.**

Für Daumenradius-Ausweitung (C nach H)　　For Thumb-extension (C to B)　　Pour l'extension du pouce (Do à Si)
Soldaten (S. 7)　　　　　　　　Soldiers (p. 7)　　　　　　Soldats (p. 7)

3.

STACCATO-NOTENMUSTER	STACCATO NOTE-PATTERNS	EXEMPLE DE NOTE EN STACCATO

Marsch der Zwerge (S. 8)　　　March of the Dwarfs (p. 8)　　　March des nains (p. 8)

4a.　　　　　　　　　**4b.**

FINGERGELENKIGKEITSÜBUNG	FINGER DRILL	EXERCICE DE DOIGT

Wiegenlied (S. 9)　　　　　Lullaby (p. 9)　　　　　Berceuse (p. 9)

5.

Weißes Kaninchen (S. 10)   **White Rabbit (p. 10)**   **Petit lapin blanc (p. 10)**

6.

Gespenster (S. 11)   **Sprites (p. 11)**   **Fantômes (p. 11)**

7.

Jump,   run   a‑long and   stay!
Spring,   lauf ein Stück und   bleib!
Sau ‑   tez fi ‑ lez   et   stop!

TAKTMUSTER ZUM MITKLATSCHEN   TIME PATTERNS TO CLAP   EXEMPLES DE MESURES A BATTRE

Die Eisenbahn (S. 13)   **Steam Train (p. 13)**   **Train à vapeur (p. 13)**

8.

Im Gebirge (S. 14)   **In the Highlands (p. 14)**   **Dans le montaignes (p. 14)**

9.

Übe Staccato aus dem Handgelenk: Practise wrist-staccato: Etudiez le staccato du poignet:

10.

FINGERGELENKIGKEITSÜBUNG   FINGER DRILL   EXERCICE DE DOIGT

11.

A and D Minor chords to end a piece (p. 11 & 12)
A- und D-Moll-Akkorde am Schluß eines Stückes (S. 11 u. 12)
La et Ré accords en mineur pour terminer un morceau (p. 11 et 12)

A triplet ending in G (p. 18)
Endung mit Triole in G (S. 18)
Un triolet se terminant en Sol (p. 18)

12a.   **12b.**

4/02 (43992)   B. & Co. Ltd. 22222   Printed and bound in Great Britain by Caligraving Limited